HÄNDEL • C. P. E. BACH • HAYDN
PURCELL • A. SCARLATTI • WEBER

CON VARIAZIONI

Easy Piano Pieces • Leichte Klavierstücke
Pièces faciles pour piano • Könnyű zongoradarabok

Compiled and edited by • Zusammengestellt und herausgegeben von
Rédigé et édité par • Összeállította és közreadja

LAKOS Ágnes

EDITIO MUSICA BUDAPEST

Universal Music Publishing Editio Musica Budapest Ltd.
H-1370 Budapest, P.O.B. 322 • Tel.: (361) 236-1100 • Telefax: (361) 236-1101
E-mail: emb@emb.hu • Internet: http://www.emb.hu

Sonatina

Johann Anton André
(1775–1842)

Z. 14 801

Allegretto vivace

Sonatina

Jiři Antonín (Georg Anton) Benda
(1722–1795)

La Folia

Alessandro Scarlatti
(1660–1725)

4.

Variazioni

Friedrich Kuhlau
(1786–1832)

Tyrolian song – Tirolerlied – Chant tyrolien – Tiroli dal

Friedrich Kuhlau

Var. 4

Sarabande

Georg Friedrich Händel
(1685–1759)

Var. 2

Menuett

(Wolfgang Amadeus Mozart: *Don Giovanni*)

Louis Köhler
(1820–1886)

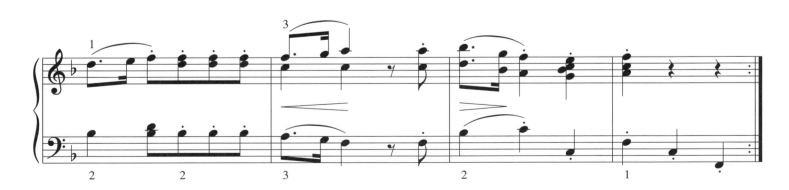

Variazione

Prélude varié

Johann Wilhelm Häßler
(1747–1822)

Chaconne

Johann Caspar Ferdinand Fischer
(1665–1746)

Chaconne

Johann Pachelbel
(1653–1706)

Gavotte

Johann Pachelbel

Var. 1

Var. 2

Ground in d

Henry Purcell
(1659–1695)

Ground in G

Henry Purcell

Ground in c

Henry Purcell

Allegretto

Joseph Haydn
(1732–1809)

Swiss song – Schweizerlied – Chant suisse – Svájci dal

("Steh' nur auf, du junger Schweizerbue")

Carl Czerny
(1791–1857)

Variazioni
(Vincenzo Bellini: *La sonnambula*)

Carl Czerny

Variationen

("Ich schlief, da träumte mir")

Carl Philipp Emanuel Bach
(1714–1788)

Var. 2

Var. 3

Var. 4

44

Tempo di minuetto

Andante con variazioni

Carl Maria von Weber
(1786–1826)

Var. 2
Minore

Var. 3

Allegretto

Small variations on a Russian theme
Kleine Variationen über ein russisches Thema
Petites variations sur un thème russe
Kis variációk egy orosz témára

Samuel Majkapar
(1867–1938)

Canon
Tempo di Tema

Contents – Inhalt – Table – Tartalom